A collecti[on]

WORDS EDITION

Pacific Press® Publishing Association
Nampa, Idaho
Oshawa, Ontario, Canada

Edited by Tim Lale
Designed by Dennis Ferree
Cover art by Steve Lanto

NOTE: All attempts have been made to find the copyright owners of songs in this book. Copyright owners who find an uncredited song to which they have rights should contact the copyright administrator at (208) 465-2500.

ISBN 13: 978-0-8163-1818-6
ISBN 10: 0-8163-1818-2

Additional copies of this book may be purchased at
http://www.adventistbookcenter.com

09 10 11 12 • 5 4 3 2

Preface

Since 1962, campers have attended Big Lake Youth Camp and enjoyed spine-tingling activities, awe-inspiring campfires, and life-changing spiritual relationships. Yet in spite of the incredible activities available, campers consistently tell us that their favorite thing about camp is campfire singing! Their singing focuses on knowing God, living His will, and doing so in an enthusiastic way. Whether the songs

Monte Torkelsen and Rick Silvestri

are lively or reflective, the singing at Big Lake has become one of the significant components of the camp's ministry to lead kids to Christ.

Throughout the year dozens of requests come into the Big Lake office for copies of the music for these songs that campers would like to continue singing in their schools and churches. In many cases, music for these songs has not even been written down, and for the songs already published, copyright laws have prevented our being able to fulfill these requests—until now!

In your hands you hold over thirty years of singing history from Big Lake. Countless songs have come and gone but others have endured as favorites. These favorites and many of the latest songs have been gathered into this collection of Big Lake's best, compiled and arranged by Oregon Conference Youth Department associate directors Rick Silvestri and Monte Torkelsen. Undoubtedly you will find this collection of songs one of the finest available for kids, youth, and young adults alike.

Contents

Shine

Peter Furler and Steve Taylor

Shine,
Make 'em wonder what you got,
Make 'em wish that they were not
On the outside looking bored.
Shine,
Let it shine before all men,
Let 'em see good works and then
Let 'em glorify the Lord.

(repeat)

Shine!

Blindman

Yohann Anderson

The blind man stood on the way and he cried,
The blind man stood on the way and he cried,
The blind man stood on the way and he cried,
Sayin' oh, oh, oh,

(chorus)
Show me the way,
Show me the way,
Show me the way,
The way to go home.

The rich man stood on the way and he cried,
The rich man stood on the way and he cried,
The rich man stood on the way and he cried,
Sayin' oh, oh, oh,

(chorus)

Show me the truth . . .

Lazarus stood on the way and he cried,
Lazarus stood on the way and he cried,
Lazarus stood on the way and he cried,
he cried, oh, oh, oh,

(chorus)

Show me the life . . .

Jesus stood on the way and He cried,
Jesus stood on the way and He cried,
Jesus stood on the way and He cried,
Sayin' oh, oh, oh,

(chorus)

I am the way . . .

3   Sandy Land
Karen Lafferty

Don't build your house on the sandy land.
Don't build it too near the shore.
Well, it might be kind of nice,
But you'll have to build it twice.
Oh, you'll have to build your house once more.

(chorus)
You better build on the Rock, *(clap, clap)*
Make a good foundation on a solid spot.
Oh, the storms may come and go,

But the peace of God you will know.

Joy! 4

Amy Grant

(verse 1)
I've got the
Joy, joy, joy, joy, joy, joy!
I've got the
Joy, joy, joy, joy, joy, joy!
I've got the
Joy, joy, joy, joy,
Joy! Joy! Joy! ("two, three, four")

(chorus)
Down in my heart, *(clap, clap)*
Down in my heart, *(clap, clap)*
Down in my heart to stay,
Down in my heart to stay.

(verse 2)
I've got the love ... *(repeat as above)*

(verse 3)
I've got the light ... *(repeat as above)*

Fear Not 5

Phil Pringle

(chorus)
Fear not, *(clap, clap)* for I am with you,
Fear not, *(clap, clap)* for I am with you,

Fear not, *(clap, clap)* for I am with you,
Says the Lord.

(repeat)

(verse)
I have redeemed you, I've called you by name.
Child, you are mine.
And when you walk through the water
I will be there
And through the flame, and you'll not be drowned
And you'll not be burned, for I am with you.

(chorus)

6   Praise Him, Raise Him

Dan Carson

I will bless the Lord at all times,
His praise shall be in my mouth.
Alleluia, alleluia.
My soul will brag in the Lord,
The humble hear and rejoice.
Alleluia, alleluia.
O magnify the Lord,
Lift His holy name. ("Amen!")

(chorus)
You got to praise Him, raise Him,
Get together and sing and shout it.
He's the reason that we're standin', jammin'.
Get up and put your hands together. *(five claps)*
Let everything that breathes
Come now and praise the Lord.

Sing for joy in the Lord, all ye righteous ones.
Alleluia, alleluia.
His praise is becoming to you. Give thanks to the Lord.
Alleluia, alleluia.
Sing praises to Him with the band,
Sing to Him a new song. ("Amen!")

Your Everlasting Love 7

Bill Batstone

Your everlasting love is higher, higher,
Higher than the sky.
Your everlasting love is higher, higher,
Higher than the sky, higher than the sky.
O the wonder of Your everlasting love
Is higher than the sky.

Your everlasting love is deeper, deeper,
Deeper than the sea.
Your everlasting love is deeper, deeper,
Deeper than the sea, deeper than the sea.
O the wonder of Your everlasting love
Is deeper than the sea.

Higher than the heavens above
Is the glory of Your wonderful love.
I'm lost in the mystery of Your everlasting love,
Your everlasting love.

Your everlasting love is reaching, reaching,
Reaching out to me.
Your everlasting love is reaching, reaching,
Reaching out to me, reaching out to me.

O the wonder of Your everlasting love
Is reaching out to me.

8 Seek First

Amy Grant and Wes King

(chorus)
Seek *(clap)* first *(clap, clap)* the kingdom of heaven,
And *(clap)* all *(clap, clap)* shall be added.
Seek *(clap)* first *(clap, clap)* the kingdom of heaven,
And *(clap)* all *(clap, clap)* shall be added.

(verse)
They say we need money and power,
They say there's no God up above.
Don't they know our Friend in high places?
Nothing can be stronger than love.

(chorus)

(Nos. 9, 10, 11, and 12 are usually sung as a medley)

9 I'm Gonna Sing, Sing, Sing

Public Domain

I'm gonna sing, sing, sing.
I'm gonna shout, shout, shout.
I'm gonna sing, I'm gonna shout, praise the Lord!
When the gates are open wide,
I'm gonna sit at Jesus' side.
I'm gonna sing, I'm gonna shout, praise the Lord!

Swing Low, Sweet Chariot

10

Public Domain

Swing low, sweet chariot,
Comin' for to carry me home.
Swing low, sweet chariot,
Comin' for to carry me home.

When the Saints Go Marching In

11

Public Domain

Oh when the saints go marching in,
Oh when the saints go marching in.
Oh Lord, I want to be in that number,
When the saints go marching in.

This Train Is Bound for Glory

12

Public Domain

This train is bound for glory, this train.
This train is bound for glory, this train.
This train is bound for glory,
Get on board and I'll tell you the story.
This train is bound for glory, this train.

13 With Christ in the Vessel

Herman Voss

(verse)
With Christ in the vessel we can smile at the storm,
Smile at the storm, smile at the storm.
With Christ in the vessel we can smile at the storm
As we go sailing home.

(chorus)
Sailing, sailing home.
Sailing, sailing home.
With Christ in the vessel we can smile at the storm
As we go sailing home.

14 A-Ha! Lelujah

Rob Evans and Roger Thrower

(chorus)
A-Ha! Lelujah, A-Ha! Lelujah, A-Ha! Lelujah,
Shout to the Lord!
A-Ha! Lelujah, A-Ha! Lelujah, A-Ha! Lelujah,
Shout to the Lord!

Clap your hands, ev'rybody now,
Like the trees that serve the Lord.
Lift your voice with a mighty shout,
Louder than the oceans roar!

(chorus)

Stomp your feet, ev'rybody now,
Like the mountains that praise the Lord.
Lift your voice with a mighty shout,
Louder than volcanoes roar!

Let There Be Light 15

Karl Anthony

(verse)
Let there be light,
Illuminate me.
Let there be light,
Illumine my soul.
Let there be light
For all the world around me.
I open my heart and watch it grow.
I open my heart and let it flow.

(chorus)
Let it flow, let it flow.
It's a light that shines within my soul.
Let it flow, let it flow.
It's a miracle.
Let there be light.

(repeat verse and chorus)

(last line of second chorus)
Let there be light!

Let Us Come Together 16

Unknown

(verse)
Let us come together,
Praise the name of Jesus.

All you people of the earth come and see.
Let us come together,
Praise the name of Jesus.
All you people of the earth come and hear.
Joy is like the sunshine,
And it's raining down upon us.
Joy is like a golden crown.
Let us come together,
Praise the name of Jesus.

(chorus)
Hallelujah! *(clap, clap)*
   Hallelujah! *(clap, clap)*
Hallelujah! *(clap, clap)*
   Hallelujah! *(clap, clap)*
Hallelujah! *(clap, clap)*
   Hallelujah! *(clap, clap)*
Hallelujah! *(clap, clap)*
   Hallelujah! *(clap, clap)*

17   I Like Bananas

Moyer Mudcheck

(chorus)
I like bananas,
I think that mangoes are sweet.
I like papayas ("Papayas!")
But nothing can beat
That sweet love of God.

(verse)
I was walking 'round in circles five miles an hour.
Tryin' to get my way back to my heavenly Father.
The world tasted sweet,
But then it turned sour.
Then I let Him in and received His power!

(chorus)

Happy All the Time

(I'm Inright, Outright)

Capt. Alan Price

I'm inright, outright, upright, downright
Happy all the time.
I'm inright, outright, upright, downright
Happy all the time.
Since Jesus Christ came in,
I gave my heart to Him.
I'm inright, outright, upright, downright
Happy all the time.

Big Red Bus

Kevin Brusett

I wanna ride on a big red bus
With Jesus Christ at the wheel.
I wanna live my life on faith and love
And the things that I know are real.
They say that life is a hard place, ("Hard place!")
But I got a ride I can trust. ("Whee-hee!")
I'm headin' homeward and I'm heaven bound
'Cause I'm ridin' on a big red b-b-b-b-bus.

(chorus)
    Let me ride
    Ride
    Ride
    On the Big Red Bus.

The bus is red 'cause the blood He shed
Is what sets me free.

I'm ridin' on the price He paid
When He died on Calvary.
They say that life is a hard place, ("Hard place!")
But I got a ride I can trust. ("Whee-hee!")
I'm headin' homeward and I'm heaven bound
'Cause I'm ridin' on a big red b-b-b-b-bus.

(chorus)

20   Where Do I Go?

Amy Grant

(chorus)
Where do I go when I need a shelter?
Where do I go when I need a friend?
Where do I go when I need some helpin'?
Where do I go? Back on my knees again.

Ask me this question, I'll tell you no lies:
"How did I get this fire in my life?"
All is not certain, but I will get by.
Listen, and I'll tell you why.

(chorus)

Sure as the winter comes after the fall,
Sure as true love tears down any wall.
Jesus is able to carry it all,
He will answer our call.

(chorus)

Hallelu, Hallelu

Percy Crawford

Hallelu, hallelu, hallelu, hallelujah!
Praise ye the Lord!
Hallelu, hallelu, hallelu, hallelujah!
Praise ye the Lord!
Praise ye the Lord!
Hallelujah!
Praise ye the Lord!
Hallelujah!
Praise ye the Lord!
Hallelujah!
Praise ye the Lord!

Touching Heaven, Changing Earth

Reuben Morgan

(verse 1)
We will seek Your face almighty God,
Turn and pray for You to heal our land.
Father, let revival start in us,
That ev'ry heart may know Your kingdom come.

(chorus)
Lifting up the name of the Lord
In power and in unity.
We will see the nations turn,
Touching heaven, changing earth.

(second chorus only)
Touching heaven, changing earth.
Touching heaven, changing earth.

(verse 2)
Never looking back we'll run the race,
Giving You our lives we'll gain the prize.
We will take the harvest giv'n to us.
Although we sow in tears we'll reap in joy.

(chorus)

23   I've Got a River of Life

L. Casebolt and Betty Carr Pulkingham

I've got a river of life flowing out of me.
Makes the lame to walk and the blind to see.
Opens prison doors, sets the captives free.
I've got a river of life flowing out of me.

Spring up O well, within my soul.
Spring up O well, and make me whole.
Spring up O well, and give to me
That life abundantly.

24   For God So Loved Us

Big Lake Youth Camp Music Performance class

(verse)
For God so loved us that He gave us His Son,
That whosoever believes shall not die.
But live forever in His arms of mercy.
He came and died so I could be forever His child.

(chorus)
Nothing to fear, no more tears.
Love has come and rescued me.
So I die to myself and now Jesus lives in me.

Ha-la-la-la-la   25

David Graham

(chorus)
Ha-la-la-la-la la-la le-lu-jah,
Ha-la-la-la-la la-le lu-jah,
Ha-la-la-la-la la-la le-lu-jah,
Ha-la-la-la-la la-la le lu-jah!

(verse 1)
Clap, clap a hand, clap a hand next to you.
Clap, clap a hand, clap a hand next to you.
Clap, clap a hand, clap a hand next to you.
Clap, clap a hand, clap a hand—next to you!

(chorus)

(verse 2) *(shake someone's hand)*
Jesus is a friend, is a friend unto you ...

(chorus)

(verse 3) *(be careful—just for fun)*
Squeeze, squeeze a knee, squeeze a knee next to you ...

(chorus)

(verse 4)
Rub, rub a back, rub a back next to you ...

26   King Jesus Is All

(chorus)
King Jesus is all, my all in all,
And I know that He'll answer me when I call.
He's walkin' by my side, I'm satisfied.
King Jesus is all, my all in all.

(verse)
I went out to meet the Lord.
I got down on my knees.
I said my very first prayer.
You know, the Holy Ghost He met me there.
I stood on the Rock, the Rock was sound.
Ooo the love of God it came a-tumbling down.
You ask me how I know that He saved my soul.
I dug down deep, and I found pure gold.

(chorus)
Yes, He's all, my all in all,
And I know that He'll answer me when I call.
He's walkin' by my side, I'm satisfied.
King Jesus is all, my all in all.

27   Over and Over

Roger J. Hughes

(verse)
Over the sea, over the sea,
Jesus, Savior, pilot me.
Over the sea, over the sea,
Over the jasper sea.

(chorus)
Over and over, like a mighty sea.
Flows the love of Jesus, flowing over me.

Silver and Gold

Unknown

Peter and John went to pray.
They met a lame man on the way.
He held out his palms, and he asked for some alms,
And this is what Peter did say:

"Silver and gold have I none,
But what I have I give thee.
In the name of Jesus Christ of Nazareth,
Rise up and walk!"

(chorus)
He went walking and leaping and praising God,
Walking and leaping and praising God.
"In the name of Jesus Christ of Nazareth,
Rise up and walk!"

28

Friends

Deborah D. Smith and Michael W. Smith

(verse 1)
Packing up the dreams God planted
In the fertile soil of you;
Can't believe the hopes He's granted
Means a chapter in your life is through.

(bridge)
But we'll keep you close as always;
It won't even seem you're gone.
'Cause our hearts in big and small ways
Will keep the love that keeps us strong.

(chorus)
And friends are friends forever
If the Lord's the Lord of them.

29

And a friend will not say "never"
'Cause the welcome will not end.
Though it's hard to let you go,
In the Father's hands we know
That a lifetime's not too long
To live as friends.

(verse 2)
With the faith and love God's given,
Springing from the hope we know.
We will pray the joy you'll live in
Is the strength that now you show.

30   Get Down

Tyler Burkum, Ben Cissell, Bob Herdman,
Will McGinniss, Stuart Mark Allen

(verse 1)
In your weakness He is stronger,
In your darkness He shines through.
When you're cryin' He's your comfort,
When you're all alone He'll carry you.

(chorus)
I get down, He lifts me up,
I get down, He lifts me up,
I get down, He lifts me up,
I get down.
I get down, He lifts me up,
I get down, He lifts me up,
I get down, He lifts me up,
I get down.

(Nos. 31 and 32 are usually sung as a medley)

He's Alive Again 31

Shawn Craig

He's alive again, oh the stone's been rolled away.
He's alive again. He's no longer where He lay.
He's alive again. I can hear the angels say,
"Let all the world rejoice, everyone lift up his voice."
Let all the world rejoice, He's alive.

I Will Call Upon the Lord 32

Michael O'Shields

I will call upon the Lord,
Who is worthy to be praised.
So shall I be saved from my enemies
I will call upon the Lord.
The Lord liveth, and blessed be the Rock, *(clap, clap)*
and let the God of my salvation be exalted.
The Lord liveth, and blessed be the Rock, *(clap, clap)*
and let the God of my salvation be exalted.

Jesus Is a River of Love 33

Dallas Holm

Well my Jesus is a river of love,
And He flows from heaven above.
He'll take ev'ry sin that you have,
And He'll wash it away, wash it away.

J-J-J-Jump in the water today.
You won't drown if you learn how to pray.
Well my Jesus is a river of love,
And He's flowin' your way.

34 Be Bold, Be Strong

Morris Chapman

Be bold, be strong,
For the Lord your God is with you.
Be bold, be strong,
For the Lord your God is with you.
Do not be afraid.
Do not be dismayed.
Walk in faith and victory.
Walk in faith and victory,
For the Lord your God is with you.

35 Give God a Hand

Cyrus "Buddy" Kalb, arr. Larry Mayfield

(chorus)
Give God a hand for all He's done.
He gave us life and His only Son.
Let's all stand up, give God a hand. *(five claps)*
Give God a hand for the victories
And all He's won in you and me.
Let's all stand up, give God a hand. *(five claps)*

(Verses are spoken by one person, usually the song leader. Each verse has a phrase that either [1] all say together or [2] divide up singers into three groups and give each one phrase to shout.)

"When we see a hard-fought football game
And somebody scores, we shout his name,
And all the people stand and clap and cheer: ("YAHOO!")
Well, in the game of life, my friend,
It's been hard fought and it's near the end,
And the score is God seven million, Satan nothin'!"

(chorus)

"When we see actors upon the stage
And you hear truth in the words they say,
When the curtain falls, we call the author's name:
("LIKE SHAKESPEARE!")
As I see the play of life unfold,
I see it's just like the Bible told,
And I want to praise the Author before the end!"

(chorus)

If most folks went to the games or plays,
I believe they'd be downright amazed to hear
They couldn't cheer or clap their hands: ("GOOD GRIEF!")
And most folks think the house of God
Is a place to snooze and snore and nod.
Let's wake 'em all up with the joyful noise of praise!

(chorus)

36 My God Is So Great

Public Domain

My God is so great,
So strong and so mighty,
There's nothing my God cannot do! *(clap clap)*
My God is so great,
So strong and so mighty,
There's nothing my God cannot do! *(clap clap)*
The mountains are His.
The valleys are His.
The stars are His handiwork too.
My God is so great,
So strong and so mighty,
There's nothing my God cannot do! *(clap clap)*

37 We Are Soldiers

Unknown

(chorus)
We are soldiers in the army.
We have to fight
And though we have to die,
We gotta hold, hold up the blood-stained banner.
We got to hold it up until we die.

(verse)
Oh well the girls [boys, staff, teacher] they were the
    soldiers.
They had their hands on the gospel plow.
One day they got old,
They couldn't fight anymore.
They said, ("Stand up and fight anyhow!")
Oh

Pharaoh, Pharaoh

Tony Sbrana

(chorus)
Pharaoh, Pharaoh,
O baby (won't you) let my people go!
Yeah, yeah, yeah.
Pharaoh, Pharaoh,
O baby (won't you) let my people go!
Yeah, yeah, yeah.

Well a burnin' bush told me the other day
That I should come over here and stay.
That I gotta get my people out of Pharaoh's hand
And lead them all to the promised land.
I said…

(chorus)

Well-a me 'n God's people comin' to the Red Sea,
And Pharaoh's army comin' after me.
I raised my rod and stuck it in the sand,
And all of God's people walked across dry land.
I said…

(chorus)

Well-a Pharaoh's army is a-comin' too,
So what do you think that I did do?
I raised my rod and I cleared my throat,
And all of Pharaoh's army did the dead man's float.
I said…

(chorus)

Let my people go! ("Free!")

39 Who's the King of the Jungle?

Annie Bush Spiers

Who's the King of the jungle? *(monkey sound)*
Who's the King of the sea? ("Wa, wa, wa!")
Who's the King of the universe, the jungle and the sea?

(chorus)
I'll tell you J-E-S-U-S, ("Yes!")
He's the King of me.
He's the King of the universe,
(after verse 1) The jungle and the sea.
(after verse 2) The forest and the trees.
(after verse 3) The desert and the swamp.
(after verse 4) The backyard and the house.

Who's the King of the forest? ("Roar!")
Who's the King of the trees? ("Ca, ca, ca!")
Who's the King of the universe,
The forest and the trees?

(chorus)

Who's the King of the desert? ("Sss!")
Who's the King of the swamp? ("Chomp!") *(slap)*
Who's the King of the universe,
The desert and the swamp?

(chorus)

Who's the King of the backyard? ("Ruff, ruff!")
Who's the King of the house? ("Meow!")
Who's the King of the universe,
The backyard and the house?

(chorus)

I'm Yours, Lord

40

Gary Chapman

(chorus)
I'm Yours, Lord,
Everything I've got, everything I am,
Everything I'm not.
I'm Yours, Lord, try me now and see,
See if I can be completely Yours.

My life and my love I leave in Your hands;
I'll gladly perform as Your will demands.
I know it's not much, Your gift to repay;
But it's all I can give and all I can say:

(chorus)

You put in us all desire to belong,
To join with Your strength and thus become strong.
With that thought in mind, I reach for the prize;
I lift up my voice to reemphasize,

(chorus)

He Is the Lord

41

(Show Your Power)

Kevin Prosch

He is the Lord, and He reigns on high.
  He is the Lord.
Spoke into the darkness, created the light.
  He is the Lord.
Who is like unto Him, never ending in days?
  He is the Lord.

He comes in pow'r when we call on His name.
　　He is the Lord.

(chorus)
Show Your power, O Lord, our God.
Show Your power, O Lord, our God, our God.

Your gospel, O Lord, is the hope of our nation.
　　You are the Lord.
It's the power of God for our salvation.
　　You are the Lord.
We ask not for riches but look to the cross.
　　You are the Lord.
And for our inheritance give us the lost.
　　You are the Lord.

42　Oh Fill It Up

Unknown

(chorus)
(guys)　　　　　(girls)
Oh fill it up.　(Fill it up and let it overflow.)
Oh fill it up.　(Fill it up and let it overflow.)
Oh fill it up.　(Fill it up and let it overflow,)
(all) Let it overflow with love.

Oh Zacchaeus. (Zacchaeus was a wee little man.)
A little man. (A little man was he.)
Not very big. (Climbed up in a sycamore tree)
For the Lord he wanted to see.

Amazing grace. (Amazing grace how sweet the sound.)
How sweet the sound. (That saved a wretch like me.)
A wretch like me. (I once was lost but now I'm found,)
Was blind but now I see.

Oh what a friend. (What a friend we have in Jesus.)
Oh what a friend. (All our sins and griefs to bear.)
Our griefs to bear. (What a privilege to carry)
Everything to God in prayer.

Salt and Light   43

Amy Grant and Wes King

(group 1)   (group 2)
We all need a little salt, (Need a little salt)
Need a little light,   (Need a little light)
Need a hopeful word, (Need a hopeful word)
(all) Shining bright.
We can be a little salt, (Be a little salt)
Be a little light,   (Be a little light)
In this darkened world, (In this darkened world) We can
(all) Shine, oh, oh, shine so bright.
Shine, oh, oh, just like the starlight.
Shine, oh, oh, shine,
Shine, oh, oh, shine the light.

I Believe in You Now   44

Wayne Kirkpatrick and Michael W. Smith

(verse 1)
Once upon a time
I was faithless, running blind
Through the valley of the lost.
So now you find it rather strange
When you hear me claim the name
Of the One who bears the cross.

(chorus)
And I say,
I believe in You now,
Your light is showing me how.
I used to walk in the shadows of doubt,
But I believe in You now.

(verse 2)
Will there ever come a day
When you follow in the way
Of the truth that sets you free?
To where the thunder of a voice,
And the echo of a choice
Will bring you to your knees?
No longer running through the night,
A conversion to the light
Giving way to disbelief.

(chorus)

45 Hiya, Hiya,

Rev. Isaac G. W. Balinda

(chorus)
Cast your burdens *(three claps)* on Jesus *(three claps)*
For He cares *(three claps)* for you. *(three claps)*
Cast your burdens *(three claps)* on Jesus *(three claps)*
For He cares *(three claps)* for you. *(three claps)*

Higher, higher, higher, higher, higher,
Higher, higher, higher, higher.
Lift Jesus higher, higher.
Higher, higher, higher, higher, higher,

Higher, higher, higher, higher,
Lift Jesus higher.

Lower, lower, lower, lower, lower,
Lower, lower, lower, lower.
Send Satan lower, lower.
Lower, lower, lower, lower, lower,
Lower, lower, lower, lower,
Send Satan lower.

Faithful One   **46**

Brian Doerkson

(verse)
Faithful One, so unchanging.
Ageless One, You're my Rock of peace.
Lord of all, I depend on You.
I call out to You again and again.
I call out to You again and again.

(chorus)
You are my Rock in times of trouble.
You lift me up when I fall down.
All through the storm Your love is the anchor,
My hope is in You alone.

Take Me to the Rock   **47**

Jon Ciccarelli

(verse 1)
Take me to the Rock that is higher than I.
Take me to the Rock that is higher.

(chorus)
You are my hope and my strength.
You are my glory and my grace.
Only in You can I find rest and be whole.

(verse 2)
Break me on the Rock that is higher than I.
Break me on the Rock that is higher.

(chorus)

(verse 3)
Build me on the Rock that is higher than I.
Build me on the Rock that is higher.

(repeat verse 1)

48 Forgiven and Free

Unknown

(verse)
There once was a man
Who was more than a man.
He came to give freedom and lend us a hand.
He came without ending, eternity pending,
His love is the theme of our song.

(chorus)
I'm in God, and God's in me.
Don't know all the answers, but in Him I believe.
I'm in God, and God's in me.
I'm nowhere near perfect,
But in Him I'm forgiven and free!

Open the Eyes of My Heart

Paul Baloche

(verse)
Open the eyes of my heart, Lord.
Open the eyes of my heart.
I want to see You,
I want to see You.

(repeat)

(chorus)
See You high and lifted up.
Shining in the light of Your glory.
Pour out Your power and love
As we sing Holy, Holy, Holy.

(girls' part)
Holy, Holy, Holy.
Holy, Holy, Holy.
Holy, Holy, Holy, I want to see You.

(repeat girls' part)

(repeat verse)

(Nos. 50 and 51 are usually sung as a medley)

Humble Thyself

Bob Hudson

Humble thyself in the sight of the Lord.
   (echo) (Humble thyself in the sight of the Lord.)
Humble thyself in the sight of the Lord.
   (Humble thyself in the sight of the Lord.)

And He (and He) shall lift (shall lift) you up
Higher and higher
And He (and He) shall lift (shall lift) you up.

Kneel and pray in the sight of the Lord.
   (Kneel and pray in the sight of the Lord.)
Kneel and pray in the sight of the Lord.
   (Kneel and pray in the sight of the Lord.)
And He (and He) shall lift (shall lift) you up
Higher and higher
And He (and He) shall lift (shall lift) you up.

Sing a new song in the sight of the Lord.
   (Sing a new song in the sight of the Lord.)
Sing a new song in the sight of the Lord.
   (Sing a new song in the sight of the Lord.)
And He (and He) shall lift (shall lift) you up
Higher and higher
And He (and He) shall lift (shall lift) you up.

51   Awesome God

Rich Mullins

Our God is an awesome God.
He reigns from heaven above
With wisdom, pow'r, and love.
Our God is an awesome God.

Refiner's Fire

Brian Doerksen

(verse)
Purify my heart,
Let me be as gold and precious silver.
Purify my heart,
Let me be as gold, pure gold.

(chorus)
Refiner's fire, my heart's one desire
Is to be holy,
Set apart for You, Lord.
I choose to be holy,
Set apart for You, my master,
Ready to do Your will.

Father God

Marc Schelske

(verse)
Father God, just for today,
Help me walk Your narrow way.
Help me stand when I could fall,
Lend me the strength to hear Your call.

(chorus)
May my steps be worship,
May my thoughts be praise,
May my words bring honor to Your name.
May my steps be worship,
May my thoughts be praise,
May my words bring honor to Your name.

54 Stand Up and Shout It

Public Domain

Is there anybody here who loves my Jesus?
Anybody here who loves my God?
I want to know,
I want to know,
Do you love my God?

(repeat)

Stand up, stand up for Jesus
Ye soldiers of the cross.
Lift high His royal banner,
It must not suffer loss.
From victory unto victory,
His army shall He lead.
Till ev'ry foe is vanquished
And Christ is Lord indeed.

Stand up and shout it if you love my Jesus.
Stand up and shout it if you love my God.
I want to know, I want to know,
Do you love my God?

55 I Want to Know You More

Unknown

Oh, I want to know You more,
Deep within my soul I want to know You.
Oh, I want to know You,
To feel Your heart and know Your mind.
Looking in Your eyes stirs up within me
Cries that say I want to know You,
Oh, I want to know You more.

Holiness

Scott Underwood

Holiness, holiness is what I long for.
Holiness is what I need.
Holiness, holiness is what You want from me,
Is what You want from me.

(chorus)
So take my heart and form it.
Take my mind, transform it.
Take my will, conform it
To Yours, to Yours, O Lord.

Faithfulness, faithfulness is what I long for.
Faithfulness is what I need.
Faithfulness, faithfulness is what You want from me,
Is what You want from me.

(chorus)

Righteousness, righteousness is what I long for.
Righteousness is what I need.
Righteousness, righteousness is what You want from me,
Is what You want from me.

(chorus)

In the Secret

Andy Park

In the secret, in the quiet place,
In the stillness You are there.
In the secret, in the quiet hour I wait
Only for You,
'Cause I want to know You more.

I want to know You.
I want to hear Your voice.
I want to know You more.
I want to touch You.
I want to see Your face.
I want to know You more.

I am reaching for the highest goal
That I might receive the prize.
Pressing onward, pushing ev'ry hindrance aside,
Out of my way,
'Cause I want to know You more.

58 Lean on Him

Bill Withers

(chorus)
Lean on Him when you're not strong.
He'll be your friend,
He'll help you carry on.
For it won't be long
'Til you're gonna need
Somebody to lean on.

Sometimes in our lives we all have pain,
We all have sorrow. But if we are wise,
We'll trust in the Lord, today and tomorrow.

(chorus)

If there is a load that you must bear,
That you can't carry, He'll always be there
To carry your load, if you just call Him.

(bridge)
Well just call on Jesus when you need a hand.

We all need Somebody to lean on.
And when you've got a problem,
Oh He'll understand.
We all need Somebody to lean on.

(chorus)

Be Still   59
(He Is God)
Peter Furler and Steve Taylor

Be still and know He,
Know He is holy.
Be still and know He is God.

Love Him more dearly,
See Him more clearly,
Be still and know He is God.
He is God,
He is God.

Shine Jesus Shine   60
Graham Kendrick

Lord, the light of Your love is shining,
In the midst of the darkness shining.
Jesus, Light of the world, shine upon us;
Set us free by the truth You now bring us,
Shine on me,
Shine on me.

(chorus)
Shine, Jesus, shine,
Fill this land with the Father's glory.
Blaze, Spirit, blaze,
Set our hearts on fire.
Flow, river, flow,
Flood the nations with grace and mercy;
Send forth Your Word, Lord,
And let there be light.

Lord, I come to Your awesome presence,
From the shadows into Your radiance;
By the blood I may enter Your brightness.
Search me, try me, consume all my darkness,
Shine on me,
Shine on me.

(chorus)

As we gaze on Your kingly brightness,
So our faces display Your likeness;
Ever changing from glory to glory,
Mirror'd here may our lives tell Your story,
Shine on me,
Shine on me.

(chorus)

61 Take My Life
(How Many Times)
Mac Powell

How many times have I turned away?
The number is the same as the sand on the shore.

Ev'ry time You've taken me back,
And now I pray You'll do it once more.

(chorus)
Please take from me my life
When I don't have the strength
To give it away to You.
Please take from me my life
When I don't have the strength
To give it away to You, Jesus.

How many times have I turned away?
The number is the same as the stars in the sky.
Ev'ry time You've taken me back,
And now I pray You'll do it once more.

He's Ever Over Me   **62**
(I Will Lift My Eyes)
Bob Stromberg

(verse)
I will lift my eyes to the hills and their Creator,
Who made all heaven and earth.
For He watches me, never sleeps, no never slumbers.
He's ever over me.

(chorus)
As I come and I go, I am safe for I know
That His care is sufficient for me.
Winter warmth and light, and a shady place in summer,
He's ever over me.

63

Set Me Free

Brian Vistaunet and Stephen Moor

(verse)
Lord, I'm coming again,
Bound in the chains of this world.
You and only You can set me free.
Lord, I'm coming again,
Laying it all at Your feet.
You and only You can set me free.

(chorus)
Come, Lord Jesus, make me whole.
Set me free from sin.
Come, Lord Jesus, make me whole.
Fill me with Your love again.

64

All That I Need

John Paul Trimble

My only hope is You, Jesus,
My only hope is You.
From early in the morning 'til late at night,
My only hope is You.

My only peace is You, Jesus.
My only peace is You.
From early in the morning 'til late at night,
My only peace is You.

My only joy is You, Jesus.
My only joy is You.
From early in the morning 'til late at night,
My only joy is You.

All that I need is You, Jesus.
All that I need is You.
From early in the morning 'til late at night,
All that I need is You,
All that I need is You.

Freedom

65

Kevin Brusett

(verse)
There is a place where my soul seeks refuge.
There is a place where my chains release.
There is a place where my spirit rejoices.
There is a place where my heart's set free.

(chorus)
Freedom for those who will listen.
Freedom for those who will come.
Freedom for those who accept
The grace and the love of the Son.
There is freedom, …
Freedom.

(repeat verse and chorus)

Freedom.

We Believe in You

66

John Barnett

Come down from Your holy mountain
    Like fire upon the land.
Come down from Your holy mountain
    And take my hand.

Come down from Your holy mountain
   Like fire upon the land.
Come down from Your holy mountain
   And take my hand.

(chorus)
   'Cause we believe in You,
   That Your word is true,
   That You died and rose again.
   And we believe Your blood
   Covers all our sin.
   We believe You'll come again.
   Jesus come again.

Come down from Your holy mountain
   Like water on the land.
Come down from Your holy mountain
   And take my hand.
Come down from Your holy mountain
   Like water on the land.
Come down from Your holy mountain
   And take my hand.

(chorus)

Come down from Your holy mountain
   Like wind upon the land.
Come down from Your holy mountain
   And take my hand.
Come down from Your holy mountain
   Like wind upon the land.
Come down from Your holy mountain
   And take my hand.

(chorus)

Step by Step

Beaker

Oh God, You are my God,
And I will ever praise You.
Oh God, You are my God,
And I will ever praise You.
I will seek You in the morning,
And I will learn to walk in Your ways.
And step by step You'll lead me,
And I will follow You all of my days.

I Will Worship You

By Kevin Brusett

I will worship You.
I will worship You.
I will worship You
All the days of my life,
All the days of my life.

I will die to You.
I will die to You.
I will die to You
All the days of my life,
All the days of my life.

(chorus)
You are grace upon the altar,
You are blood shed by the Lamb.
You have offered us Your kingdom.
You will love me as I am ("Yeah!")

I will worship You.
I will worship You.
I will worship You
All the days of my life,
All the days of my life.
All the days of my
All the days of my
All the days of my life.

69   Shout to the Lord

Darlene Zschech

My Jesus, my Savior,
Lord, there is none like You.
All of my days, I want to praise
The wonders of Your mighty love.

My comfort, my Shelter,
Tower of refuge and strength.
Let ev'ry breath, all that I am,
Never cease to worship You.

(chorus)
Shout to the Lord, all the earth let us sing,
Power and majesty, praise to the King;
Mountains bow down, and the seas will roar
At the sound of Your name.
I sing for joy at the work of Your hands,
Forever I'll love You, forever I'll stand.
Nothing compares to the promise I have in You.

(repeat verse)

Glory, Glory

Alton Petersen and James Ward

(verse 1)
(girls)   *(guys)*
Glory, glory. (Glory, glory.)
Hallelujah. (Hallelujah.)
Since I laid (Since I laid) *(all)* my burden down.
Glory, glory. (Glory, glory.)
Halle, *(all)* hallelujah,
Since I laid my burden down.

(verse 2)
Friends don't treat me (Friends don't treat me)
Like they used to, (Like they used to,)
Since I laid (Since I laid) *(all)* my burden down.
Friends don't treat me (Friends don't treat me)
Like they, *(all)* like they used to.
Since I laid my burden down.

(chorus)
(all)
Singing glory, glory,
Glory hallelujah.
Glory, glory,
Glory hallelujah.
Hallelujah, hallelujah, hallelujah, hallelujah,
Since I laid my burden down.

(verse 3)
I feel better (I feel better)
So much better (So much better)
Since I laid (Since I laid) *(all)* my burden down.
I feel better (I feel better),
So much, *(all)* so much better
Since I laid my burden down.

71 Lord, I Lift Your Name on High

Rick Founds

(verses)
Lord, I lift Your name on high!
Lord, I love to sing Your praises.
I'm so glad You're in my life.
I'm so glad You came to save us.

(chorus)
You came from heaven to earth
To show the way,
From the earth to the cross
My debt to pay.
From the cross to the grave,
From the grave to the sky,
Lord, I lift Your name on high!

72 Family

Unknown

Family, we are family.
Jesus, He is our Lord.
And I'm so glad He's brought us all together.
I'm so glad that the Father is our God.

We share good times together.
We share the bad times too.
But I know my friends will never leave me.
That's because we were all first loved by Him.

Yes, I'm so glad He's brought us all together.
I'm so glad that the Father is our God.

Light the Fire Again   73

Brian Doerkson

Don't let my love grow cold.
I'm calling out, light the fire again.
Don't let my vision die.
I'm calling out, light the fire again.
You know my heart, my deeds.
I'm calling out, light the fire again.
I need Your discipline.
I'm calling out, light the fire again.

(chorus)
I am here to buy gold refined in the fire.
Naked and poor, wretched and blind I come.
Clothe me in white so I won't be ashamed.
Lord, light the fire again.

Seek Ye First   74

Karen Lafferty

Seek ye first the kingdom of God
And His righteousness.
And all these things shall be added unto you.
Allelu, alleluia.

Ask and it shall be given unto you.
Seek and ye shall find.
Knock and the door shall be opened unto you.
Allelu, alleluia.

Man does not live by bread alone
But by ev'ry word
That proceeds from the mouth of God.
Allelu, alleluia.

75 Arms of Love
Craig Musseau

I sing a simple song of love
To my Savior, to my Jesus.
I'm grateful for the things You've done,
My loving Savior, oh precious Jesus.
My heart is glad that You called me Your own.
There's no place I'd rather be
Than in Your arms of love,
In Your arms of love.
Holding me still, holding me near
In Your arms of love.

76 Lord, My Desire
Randy Butler

Lord, my desire is to be like You.
Say the things You say
And do the things You do.
Help me hear Your still voice
Through all the other noise.
So that I can be
All that You want me to be.

Come Just as You Are **77**

Joseph Sabolick

(verse)
Come just as you are.
Hear the Spirit call.
Come just as you are.
Come and see, come receive.
Come and live forever.

(repeat verse)

(chorus)
Life everlasting, strength for today.
Taste the Living Water and never thirst again.

(repeat verse)

My God Loves Me **78**

Unknown

My God loves me
And all the wonders I see.
The rainbow shines through my window,
My God loves me.

Make Me a Servant **79**

Kelly Willard

Make me a servant, humble and meek.
Lord, let me lift up those who are weak.
And may the prayer of my heart always be:

Make me a servant,
Make me a servant,
Make me a servant today.

80   Goodbye World
Unknown

Goodbye world, I'll stay no longer with you.
Goodbye, pleasures of sin, I'll stay no longer with you.
I've made up my mind to go God's way
For the rest of my life.
I've made up my mind to go God's way
For the rest of my life.

81   Alleluia
Jerry Sinclair

Alleluia, alleluia,
Alleluia, alleluia.
Alleluia, alleluia,
Alleluia, praise the Lord.

What a friend we have in Jesus,
All our sins and griefs to bear.
What a privilege to carry
Everything to God in prayer.

Jesus loves me this I know,
For the Bible tells me so.

Little ones to Him belong.
They are weak, but He is strong.

He is coming. He is coming.
He is coming. He is coming.
He is coming. He is coming.
He is coming, praise the Lord.

Sing Alleluia   82
Linda Stassen

Sing alleluia to the Lord.
   (Sing alleluia to the Lord.)
Sing alleluia to the Lord.
   (Sing alleluia.)
Sing alleluia, sing alleluia.
   (Alleluia.)
Sing alleluia to the Lord.

Jesus is Lord of heav'n and earth.
Jesus is Lord of heav'n and earth.
Jesus is Lord, Jesus is Lord,
Jesus is Lord of heav'n and earth.

He's coming back to take me home.
He's coming back to take me home.
He's coming back, He's coming back,
He's coming back to take me home.

83   Draw Me Close to You

Kelly Carpenter

Draw me close to You, never let me go.
I lay it all down again
To hear You say that I'm Your friend.
You are my desire. No one else will do,
'Cause no one else can take Your place,
To feel the warmth of Your embrace.
Help me find the way, bring me back to You.
Bring me back to You!

(Chorus)
You're all I want, Jesus.
You're all I ever needed.
You're all I want.
Help me know You are near.

84   Only One Thing

Jon Byron

(verse 1)
Only one thing,
Only one thing,
Only one thing is needful.
To sit at Thy feet,
To listen to Thee,
To find all I need in You.

(verse 2)
Only one thing,
Only one thing,
Only one thing is needful.
To sit at My feet,

To listen to Me,
To find all you need in Me.

(repeat verse 1, a capella)

He Knows My Name **85**
Tommy Walker

I have a Maker. He formed my heart.
Before even time began, my life was in His hands.

(chorus)
He knows my name.
He knows my ev'ry thought.
He sees each tear that falls,
And hears me when I call.

I have a Father. He calls me His own.
He'll never leave me, no matter where I roam.

(chorus)

I Love You, Lord **86**
Laurie Klein

I love You, Lord, and I lift my voice
To worship You, O my soul, rejoice!
Take joy, my King, in what You hear.
May it be a sweet, sweet sound
In Your ear.

87   Amazing Grace

John Newton/Public Domain

Amazing grace, how sweet the sound
That saved a wretch like me.
I once was lost, but now I'm found,
Was blind but now I see,
Hallelujah!

(Chorus)
Hallelujah, hallelujah.
Hallelujah, hallelujah,
Hallelujah, hallelujah.
Hallelujah, hallelu,
Hallelujah!

Jesus loves me, this I know,
For the Bible tells me so.
Little ones to Him belong,
They are weak, but He is strong,
Hallelujah!

(chorus)

When we've been there ten thousand years,
Bright shining as the sun,
We've no less days to sing God's praise
Than when we'd first begun,
Hallelujah!

(chorus)

From the Rising of the Sun   88

the Sun

Paul Deming

(verse)
From the rising of the sun
To the going down of the same,
The name of the Lord shall be praised.
From the rising of the sun
To the going down of the same,
The name of the Lord shall be praised.

(chorus)
So praise ye the Lord.
Praise ye the Lord.
From the rising of the sun
To the going down of the same,
The name of the Lord shall be praised.

Sanctuary   89

John Thompson and Randy Scruggs

Lord, prepare me to be a sanctuary,
Pure and holy, tried and true.
With thanksgiving, I'll be a living
Sanctuary for You.

90   I Want to Be Like You

Michael Christ

(chorus)
I want to be like You;
I want to follow after You;
I want to know You more, my God,
Know You, my God.

(repeat)

(bridge)
Show me Your way.
Show me Your way.
Strengthen me to follow You, my God.

(repeat chorus)

91   Jesus Is the Answer

Andrae and Sandra Crouch

Jesus is the answer for the world today.
Above Him there's no other,
Jesus is the way.

Jesus is the answer for the world today.
Above Him there's no other,
Jesus is the way.